ONE OUT OF FOUR

ONE

OUT
OF FOUR

A personal experience with cancer
by MYRTLE WILLIAMSON
Foreword by Lewis C. Sharman, M.D.

JOHN KNOX PRESS
RICHMOND, VIRGINIA

Library of Congress Catalog Card Number: 60-8201

Second printing 1961

© C. D. Deans 1960
Printed in the United States of America
7587-(20)-2991

Foreword

In these troubled days, filled with tensions, con-
flicts, and anxieties, God's people often fail to develop
a spiritual foundation for their day-to-day lives.
When called upon to meet the challenge of the
times, it is no wonder that many of us find that we
are not spiritually equipped to do so.

Here is a book with a vital and meaningful mes-
sage, a book of abiding values, which will lift the
spirit, and foster courage and faith in those who face
illness and suffering.

Here is the heartfelt story of a servant of God, who,
though afflicted with cancer which subsequently
proved to be medically incurable, possessed an un-
faltering faith and refused to give in to fear and
despair. Fortified by an inner strength and peace
which come from knowing that one is within God's
will, the author put together this book with the hope

5

that it would help others help themselves in time of trial.

My personal association with the author left an enduring spiritual impact upon me. I am certain that those who read her words will likewise gain some strength and encouragement to live the victorious life in Christ.

LEWIS C. SHARMAN, M.D.

Contents

An Explanation   9

1. SUSPICION: Am I "the fourth one"?   13

2. DISCOVERY: Cancer is a fact   23

3. REALIZATION: It must be faced   31

4. DECISION: What are the ways out?   39

5. SUSPENSE: "You have to walk it by yourself"   45

6. PRAYER: "I am not alone . . ."   49

7. A SENSE OF HUMOR: Develop it!   59

8. A NEW ADVENTURE: Find it!   63

9. THE RAZOR'S EDGE: Walk it!   69

God Bless You Every One   75

An Explanation

Dr. Lewis Sharman, attending me after an operation for advanced malignancy, said: "Your good comeback can be explained in large part by your grasp of the intangibles." He spoke of the need for helping others in similar situations, and asked me to write of the things which had helped me. Because I was grateful beyond words for the help which had come to me, I agreed to pray about the need and to see if I could write out the things which had helped me most.

As this very intimate account of one person's experience with cancer has been written, it has seemed to me that there are two hopes embodied in it: the first is the hope that it may help those who are facing a similar experience; the second is that it may help those whose loved ones have cancer or any serious illness of any kind.

A close friend, in discussing the need for such an account, said bluntly, "You know if it is to have any value, you will have to make it very personal. And you'll have to let the struggle show. It can't be just sweetness and light."

So I have made it personal . . . indecently personal in places, it seems to me. And I have tried to record faithfully the struggles which continue as well as the peace which abides.

If it helps anyone at all, I shall be repaid for the cost of exposing my weaknesses and of telling how God helped in hours of need.

MYRTLE WILLIAMSON

ONE OUT OF FOUR

1.

SUSPICION:

Am I "the fourth one"?

"Just mail me the statement, please."

Hastily I recapped my pen. Quickly I dropped it and the check on which I had begun to sign my name into my purse. Hurriedly I walked toward the door.

"Walk!" I admonished myself sternly. "Walk! Don't run! You'll be out of here in a minute."

I had to get out of that room. I had to be alone with myself. I had been ready to pay my bill in a doctor's office when suddenly an unspoken word had struck across my mind like a shattering clap of thunder. Like long, continuing peals of thunder it was now echoing and re-echoing through all the deep places of my being: "Cancer! CANCER!! *CANCER!!!*"

I reached the outside door. I opened it quickly, closed it softly, and held it tightly shut for a moment as I breathed in deeply the soft December air of sunlit Alabama.

"Why, I'm gulping air," one side of me thought in a detached, objective way, "as if I had run for miles." But immediately in the other side of me that unspoken word began its deep vibrations again.

"Just relax," again I admonished myself, but this time more gently. "Relax, you can face it in a moment."

What a difference that short half hour in the doctor's office had made in the day which had dawned so gloriously! I had awakened, one week before Christmas Day, feeling all the wonder of a bright morning. College classes had been dismissed and all the gaiety of the holiday season seemed to have crystallized into the sunlight of this glorious morning. I awoke with feelings of keen anticipation. Today's schedule was a full and happy one: there would be time for leisurely shopping and a routine checkup at the doctor's office before a luncheon-lecture with a few close friends and a group of interesting acquaintances. After that would come the fun of a long, uninterrupted afternoon and evening of wrapping gifts—always a joy! Also there was the pleasure of making decisions about the wardrobe needs for a twofold Christmas celebration. The first was to be with my niece's family, where three beloved children waited with starry eyes. The second was to be at a youth convention where I was to lead a study group; this held unusual interest and opportunity for study and personal contacts. The first happy day of an unusually happy vacation! I faced it with keen anticipation and sang Christmas carols lustily (and off key, as usual) through the bath and breakfast preparations, enjoying each moment to the full.

The joys of that morning were all the sharper because within four weeks my sabbatical year of study would begin. My registration at an Eastern university offered opportunities for study for which I had hungered for years. During the past weeks, I had made any number of different schedules in happy appreciation of limitless possibilities. Day by day I had been changing these schedules, reshaping, evaluating, weighing contents of courses, viewpoints of professors, hours of the day, days of the week, and juggling the total possibilities for achieving the greatest good from both curricular and extra-curricular activities. A dream of a professional lifetime was coming true at last! Every day was filled to the brim with glad preparation for leaving a well-loved work for a happy interlude of study and play. Life was good, and I was ready for every present joy and all that lay ahead.

"How silly," I had thought gaily as I finished my shopping, "to be going to a doctor on a day like this; I never felt better in my life. Friends constantly comment that I am the picture of health." I swung happily along the two blocks to the doctor's office in air that made walking pure delight, and laughed to myself: "This is what comes of being born into a family that has always taken its Christianity and its *doctors* seriously; on a day like this I waste a beautiful hour just to be told there is nothing wrong with me!"

How unexpectedly the mood had changed within the doctor's office! "You're half a year late," the capable gynecologist said smilingly as he looked at my card. "You are supposed to see me at least every year, you know."

"We agreed that I should come every six months," I answered. "Has it really, really been a year?"

"A year and a half." He consulted the card. "You were here in July—but July of last year," he said reprovingly.

"I felt so well that I forgot to come," I laughed. "I thought you would congratulate me for remembering when there is nothing wrong."

Later, however, as the examination progressed, I confessed that I had come because I had discovered quite by accident a small sore spot just below my armpit. The appointment had been made for the first opening, even though I felt quite sure that the small tender place was only a swollen milk gland. These had been declared harmless again and again by various doctors over a long period of years.

"But this is on the other side," the doctor informed me. "Also there is a very suspicious-looking lump in your left breast which has come since your last examination."

The examination was followed by a very serious talk in which I was advised to consult a surgeon that very day. Startled and very surprised, I protested that I had a commitment for a convention the following week; but he spoke so seriously that I left his office with a list of surgeons, and a promise that I would see one of them that very afternoon.

I had not realized the impact of that conversation upon me until I waited for the bookkeeper to give me her attention. Then suddenly the unspoken word "Cancer" had filled my entire being and had shaken my very foundations. Now I stood outside the office building and consciously tried to pull the remnants of my composure into place. A glance at my watch showed that it was time for a friend to pick me up for the lecture-luncheon as we had agreed two hours before. Two *hours?* Two lifetimes, it seemed! Cancer? I? How blind I had been to feel so confident that it could never happen to me. Suppose it was cancer, suppose it was happening to me NOW of all times?

Fortunately my friend was late. I walked rapidly away from the doctor's building toward a corner where I could watch for her approach. I wanted to run from the fact that I might have cancer; the temptation to run physically was still strong—to "panic" mentally was an even stronger urge. Sudden, unexpected forces were gripping me with such a frightening strength that my body as well as my mind trembled. I felt helpless and in my helplessness must have turned unconsciously toward God. At any rate some spiritual part of me suddenly said very quietly: "Stop it; are you or are you not a Christian? Do you or do you not really believe what you profess?"

"I don't know about me. I don't know," I answered honestly. "But I do know that God can be trusted!" So I prayed: "This is too big for me to handle, Father; please take over."

By the time Margaret's car appeared, prayer had given God a chance to still the panic, although the mind and body still felt the effect of fear. To cope with the fear, I brought it at once into the open and announced as I entered the car, "Dr. Brown found a lump in my left breast and he sounds as if he fears I may have cancer."

Margaret parked the car. As we talked together I realized how blest I was to have a friend so frank and so fearless that she could help me face facts realistically. I know that for me it was necessary to say "cancer" over and over again until it became commonplace; that because I had been so sure I would never be the one out of four to have cancer, I had no preparation, foolishly, for the fact that I might well be the fourth one.

As we talked, more and more problems raised their heads. If the specialist recommended surgery, would it be best to have it done here or to fly to a city where members of my family were near medical centers? Since there were three such cities, to which one should I go? Which surgeon should be chosen if it were best to remain in our college-university town? We agreed that time was needed for consideration before final decisions—time, and quietness of spirit to allow God to speak to my feeling of deep need. We agreed that Margaret would carry the conversational ball for us both during the luncheon and I would sit quietly until the weighing of all possibilities could help decide the course of action.

That hour at the lecture-luncheon was a cool spot in the midst of blinding heat. We found Hugh and Audrey, a young couple dear to both of us. Margaret skillfully guided the conversation to cover my silence. Audrey's sensitiveness made her immediately aware that something was wrong with me. I rested beside her secure in two accepted facts: she would ask no questions, and her prayers would immediately and constantly be joined with Margaret's and mine beneath the level of table talk. I hardly heard the conversation, but I began to feel quiet strength flowing into me, not only from Margaret and Audrey, but also from Hugh, who was sitting beside me completely unaware that anything was amiss, but blessedly solid and to be counted on when needed. As I gave thanks for friends whose love gives courage, a little of the outward calm I had been maintaining at great cost began to seep inward and to change fear to faith.

"If I am the one out of my group of four to have cancer," I affirmed silently, "God will help me bear it." And the peace which had routed the panic began to work at a deeper level on the very roots of my fear. I could think the word cancer now without crumpling up inside.

Today that luncheon is in my memory as a picture of three very real persons etched in bright light, comforting and consoling, in friendly poses against a gray blur of aching pain. It was a tiny fragment of the beloved community where strength flows from friend to friend, renewing faith without the need for words!

2.

DISCOVERY:

Cancer is a fact

And so it came to pass that I spent Christmas in the hospital.

Within two hours after the luncheon, the surgeon confirmed the gynecologist's findings and asked my permission for radical surgery if the lump proved to be malignant.

"It should come out immediately," he said. "When do you want to have it done?"

"Tomorrow," I answered, so promptly that he laughed with me. I did not tell him that waiting is the thing I do least gracefully, that suspense has ever been the hardest thing for me to bear; nor that I had come to him because I still had hopes of attending the convention when the "harmless lump" was removed, even though long-distance calls would arrange for someone to take my place, "just in case it should prove to be malignant."

Because of the holiday season, he had been able to see me immediately—a most unusual blessing. Because of the holiday season, there was a vacancy both in his schedule and in the operating room schedule. How grateful I was for these great favors which eliminated waiting! With the date of the operation settled, the hours began to have peculiar significance. At last I could legitimately *run*. Margaret says I came dashing out of the inner office to where she faithfully waited in the reception room, saying as I ran, "Come on, we have two hours to cancel all Christmas plans and get to the hospital before closing time."

Telegrams, several long-distance telephone calls, and hurried packing filled those two hours with healing activity. The telephone calls went through like magic. The persons to be seen on the campus were all in. We reached the hospital in time for all the tests, X-rays, and other preparations which leave a well person wondering how one who is ill can stand the strain of a "pre-operative" evening! There were, of course, compensations: each time I settled on my pillow thinking, "Now at last I can think this startling thing through," another hospital personage appeared with new equipment, saying, "We need . . . so and so . . . for tomorrow's operation," and I went through another experience of new bloodletting, X-raying, or something else that made facing the problem impossible. When the thinking process had been postponed six or eight times, I just shifted my mind into neutral and thought, "Goody. I can legitimately be Scarlett O'Hara now and think about this tomorrow."

In spite of my facetiousness, however, ever since the shock of the morning Paul's testimony to the Romans had been comforting me; surely, if "nothing can separate us from the love of Christ," *nothing* included cancer also. And if "in *all* these things we are more than conquerors through Christ who loves us," we can trust God for help; for cancer, it seemed to me, is little more than "just one of those things."

That night had its ludicrous side also. Because of the suddenness of my entry I had to be placed in the only available bed. This bed was in the room with a dear elderly woman, delirious from a recent broken hip. Her equally elderly husband, who was deaf, was watching her to keep her from getting up and falling. Their love and concern for each other were beautifully real. She could not bear the thought of his having to sit up all night, and he kept trying to reassure her that she was in the hospital and all would be well if only she would lie quietly in bed. Conversations like this with little variation continued over and over throughout the night:

"John, what's *that woman* doing in your bed? She

can't sleep in here with us. I'm getting up and we're going to a decent hotel right now." He answered her movements although he did not hear her words, "Lie still, dear. You're in the hospital. Don't hurt your sore hip."

"John," patting her pillow emphatically, "you come up here by me. You know it will make you sick to sit up all night. *Who* is *that woman?* You come up here or let's go home to our own beds."

"You're in the hospital, dear. Lie still; don't hurt your hip."

His love was great, so, not hearing, he kept comforting her over and over, but all her anxiety for his welfare and all her queries about *"Who* is *that woman?"* and *"What* is *that woman* doing in *your* bed?"* went unanswered.

My concern for their distress was mingled with mirth at the idea of me, a gray-haired professor of Bible in a church-related college, in the role of a bed-stealing "that woman"! Time after time fitful sleep was broken by the conversations repeated over and over; but time after time peace returned as I said, after praying for the dear old couple, "This is still too big for me to handle, Father. I'm leaving all of it in your hands."

Hospital days start early. I awoke to find the attendants busily engaged in preparations to remove the elderly lady and her bed to another room. Since my operation was scheduled first, early shots were administered at once and things began to blur. Early as it was, the college president, the head of our department, and three college professors, including the faithful Margaret, appeared briefly and disappeared. Members of my own family could not be there, but here were members of our college family, a part of the beloved community, standing by faithfully. I remember thinking sleepily, "What do persons do who do not know the covenant community?" I remember saying to Al, the department head, "I'm almost asleep," and his young hand warm on mine and his comforting voice saying, "Go to sleep. We are all praying with you." I remember the president's presence, my protest that he should have left on a trip early that morning as he had planned, and his assurance, "We shall not leave until you are all right." My last thought was thanksgiving for such friends. I slept deeply and did not know when attendants came to wheel me to the operating room.

When I awoke at six o'clock that evening, my first consciousness was of the comforting presence of Martha, a young professor of the social sciences, who was bending above me lovingly to ask if I wanted anything. My second awareness was that my entire left side was stiff with bandages. There was no doubt about it now: *I* was the fourth one in my group of four. I remember thinking wearily that I was not surprised at not being surprised at the bandages, that I must have known subconsciously that the doctors were right even though I had not given in, and that now thinking things through would have to wait— I could do nothing more now than handle the physical pain.

The next days are blurred in my memory. Fortunately the good doctors and nurses have learned how to relieve pain; intense suffering was never allowed to continue beyond a few moments. A kind of vacuum existence set in, in which I alternately slept, awoke to pain, was relieved, lay still, and slept again.

It was like riding the great waves of a boundless sea, with recurring moments of resting on the crests interspersed with deep sliding back into the depths of healing sleep. Each time I awoke there were the faces of loving friends or the skillful hands of helpful nurses and capable doctors—and a deep peace that was not of my making. I did not possess it, but it possessed me and filled me with the knowledge that the present moment demanded nothing of me. Cancer was a reality which must be faced eventually. Now I must rest and give thanks. God had led me to efficient doctors. He had sent wonderful friends to alternate with nurses around the clock. God, who had given His peace in a wonderful way, would help me face the reality of cancer when the time came. I lived as in an interlude.

The room became full of flowers. A Christmas tree and numberless gifts appeared. Friends came and went. Doctors and nurses did kindly, soothing things, and hurting kindly things. I majored in non-resistance. I rode the waves. I gave thanks for friends and the peace of God.

3.

REALIZATION:

It must be faced

As the days went by, my almost-pleasant, peace-filled sea of recurring pain and numbness passed also. The interlude ended: thought returned, and with it the temptation to fear.

Temptations come to different persons in various ways; talks with many persons have convinced me that most patients hospitalized for cancer run at least part of the entire gamut of temptations to fear.

Fear is a coward. When fear is faced freely and frankly, half the battle against him is won. But like most cowards, fear is a bully. When he is not faced, day by day, he increases his power until he rules, either consciously or unconsciously, more and more of the personality which refuses to face him. Cancer is a breeder of fear in many minds. Without the grace of God and the wisdom of an understanding doctor, escape from one of the many traps of fear is almost impossible.

The things that saved me were three. First, there was the faith that God, who had brought me through the deepest sorrows I was capable of experiencing, was in this experience with me and would work with me. Second, there was my knowledge of my own weakness which made me know that I must face fears as soon as I saw them. And third, there was the wisdom of my surgeon, who knew how much information to give me as I asked for it, and who recognized the hour when I needed to face all possibilities in the light of all known facts.

I had never met Dr. Sharman until he walked into the inner office where I waited on that first startling afternoon. I knew within minutes that he was the right surgeon for me: that patients were persons to him, not just "cases"; that he was a gentle man with the capacity to be hard and firm in necessity; and, most of all, that he knew what he was about. His quiet confidence was based on real knowledge; his quick efficiency came from much practice; and his ability to ask and willingness to answer pertinent questions gave me great confidence. The first hurdle was past: the patient trusted the doctor.

The trust was justified. I became increasingly grateful to him as he fulfilled each expectation. Although the days-in-the-ocean are blurred, I remember clearly one crest-of-the-wave visit when I asked about the lump. "I know it was malignant from all this dressing," I said, "but please tell me about it."

"It was the size of a large olive," he answered promptly, "and it was completely surrounded by scar tissue."

"That is a good sign?" I asked.

"A very good sign," he answered. "It shows your body had been fighting."

I was comforted. I thought that being encased in scar tissue meant that the cancer had not spread. I could not have taken any more information just then. He answered me truthfully. He did not burden me with more truth than I could bear.

I came into the realization of the seriousness of my case gradually through a series of incidents. When questioned about how soon I could leave the hospital and fly home, Dr. Sharman answered that he would begin X-ray treatments when my wound had healed a little more. I must have looked startled, for he patted my good shoulder and said, "You know, I always 'throw the book' at my patients."

So it was worse than I had thought. I began making statements and watching the reactions of my friends. Finally I picked a friend who I was sure would know the true extent of my disease. Watching her reaction very closely, I casually remarked how glad I was that the operation had removed all of the cancer. I knew her so well that I read the confirmation of what I had suspected in her quickly veiled look and in her too cheerful, too ready answer. I knew that I must now go back to Dr. Sharman for the whole truth. But I was not ready yet.

Have you ever had the experience of having the right person come to see you at the right time? That happened to me. A minister of whom I had heard much, but whom I had never seen, came to see me. Partly because of his personality and consecration, and partly because we knew each other through mutual friends, I found that I could discuss with him impersonally the very personal things which troubled me. The spiritual discussion and the earnest prayer which followed strengthened me. I was ready to face facts with Dr. Sharman.

"Sometime when you have time, Doctor," I said to him on an evening visit, "I'd like to face some facts with you."

"What about now?" he asked, as he reseated himself and relaxed in a leisurely fashion. "I have all the time in the world."

So we talked. I asked many questions and he answered them, the large ones and the small details, frankly and fully. I told him of the peace which had kept me when I was unable to keep myself. We talked of death and agreed that it was a gate on a far horizon through which we all pass sooner or later. Then I confessed that it was what lay between my present state and that gateway that bothered me, and asked him for the entire truth concerning all the physical possibilities of the years ahead. How grateful I was that he didn't "play pollyanna"—that he treated me as an adult who had a right to the truth, that he spoke hopefully but was honest enough to say that cancer which has invaded the lymph system was an unknown factor. He continued to answer the questions with which I plied him until I had a pretty clear picture of all the things which might be expected to happen, whether it were the complete cure for which he hoped or the return of the disease in one of several forms. He was wise in telling all the things I wanted so much to know. And he was wise in stopping my speculations.

"Suppose it does return," I mused. "I think I won't have another operation. Don't you think they just prolong suffering?"

"Whoa, there!" he answered. "You're way out in front of me. The thing to do now is to get well, not to make hypothetical solutions to problems which have not arisen."

We laughed together, and I was reproved as I knew I needed to be. The fears were all in the open now. I vaguely sensed the razor's edge upon which I must walk. I knew where my particular battle-ground would lie: I'd have to learn to live with not-knowing, with suspense—always one of my worst foes. And I'd have to begin learning to allow others to do things for me: the grace of receiving favors graciously was one I had long needed to develop.

When we had talked of commonplace things and laughed together, the doctor left his patient at ease. I had just learned that I had one chance in four, humanly speaking, of being fully cured by the operation. The sting had been taken from the hidden fears now that we had faced them, and the future lay ahead. I accepted the promise: "As thy days, so shall thy strength be." I gave thanks for a doctor who could drain fears from the mind as well as remove cancers from the body. And I fell asleep.

4.

DECISION:

What are the ways out?

It is a crucial time in a person's life when first the realization dawns that cancer is a known fact and that the outcome must be uncertain for a time. How does one react to such news? We know so little about ourselves that this is an uncertain question. I think that no one can be very sure until after the thing has happened.

During the time since I first knew that there is a 25% chance of cure for cases like mine, I have remembered many things:

I remember a classmate of mine who died on the operating table several years ago. She came to see me a short time before the operation, after we had worked together for many years, and said, "I've done everything I've wanted to do in life, and I've seen all the members of my family through their difficulties. For the first time in my life, nobody really needs me and there is nothing which at this moment I want to do." She went home, made her will, gave away or disposed in some way of all her personal possessions, went into the hospital and died before she knew she had a very advanced malignancy.

It was so like her systematic way of doing things that I could not grieve for her—I felt her spirit laughing with me as she had laughed when she was through (efficiently, triumphantly through!) with some hard assignment. She had died as she had lived: neatly, at the proper time, with no trouble for anybody! How I wished I might have gone as she did—until I remembered my cluttered files, my dresser drawers, the unburned letters, etc., ad infinitum! My life had never been like hers—how could my death be?

I remember another classmate of ours who died with cancer about the same time as M.—but she died by inches—by painful agonizing inches that brought out all the latent heroism of her wonderful spirit! The valiant bravery and splendid courage were there all along but she had felt she was a failure until she found herself able to "take it." How beautifully she *shone* during those months of pain! In the process of dying she achieved what she had longed for all her life: she became a person whose influence was felt for great good by all who knew her and many who only heard of her. If that should be my lot, how her example would strengthen me!

I remembered Alex—his high courage and his tireless energy during the three years he continued to work after his first operation. His beautiful daughter encouraged me by saying, "You know the most fruitful years of my Daddy's life came after he had cancer."

I remembered Dr. Pat, who retired in the month of May, spent a painless month in bed, and died without any pain at all at the end of June.

And I remembered 'Kenzie!—'Kenzie, who in the midst of great pain, after months of great pain, looked up at a mutual friend of ours and said, "Oh, Nelle, what if I had missed this! What if I had missed what I have learned about God through this experience of cancer!"

These all have died—as did my friend Kay who testified of God's ability to provide grace as it is needed—as did another friend who wrote a short time before her death of how wonderful it had been "to have two full years to prepare for eternity," and of how grateful she was for God's goodness to her in allowing her "time to get the grayness out of my soul."

These died in faith, with cancer. But in the circle of my close friends, there were more than a score of persons who were living as I was in the post-operative days. Some have passed the years of waiting and know themselves cured—but some still walk the razor's edge of waiting to know what the outcome will be. We have talked about the temptations which assail persons in our situations. I have talked also with several friendly doctors and nurses, and it seems to me we need to face frankly "the ways out" which present themselves.

Several nurses and doctors have told me of persons who just give up when they realize that cancer is their trouble. Despair strikes; they refuse to eat or to co-operate in any way with the healing processes; they give up before the battle starts.

Some go to the other extreme. They refuse to admit there is anything wrong with them. They persist in attempting to ignore all signs, to live as if nothing had happened, to lock the facts and fears deep inside themselves and live on the surface of the volcano as if there were no fire beneath the exterior. "Escape" literature, "escape" activities, "escape" in all its forms, fills the days.

There are those who are told the truth and refuse to accept it—who go from doctor to doctor "hoping to find out what is wrong with me." Filled with rebellion, they blame the doctors for a wrong diagnosis, and fight the doctors rather than the disease.

Then there are those who never know the truth—whose families conspire with their doctors to keep the truth from them, and who therefore miss the blessings which come when one lives in two worlds and begins to "major in things which are eternal."

There are, perhaps, as many different reactions as there are persons. The group in which my friends and I walk is perhaps the largest group: those who walk the razor's edge of not-knowing, of waiting for decision one way or the other, of being ready, as Paul wrote to the Philippians, "to depart and be with Christ" or "to remain in the flesh." It would be comparatively easy to do either one if you knew definitely which was coming; to remain equally ready for either requires a spiritual discipline which demands that we be bigger than we are. Therefore we are thrown back constantly upon God and we can enter a relationship which has such compensations that even having cancer becomes worth while.

Walking the razor's edge is costly. We shall talk of that again.

5.

SUSPENSE:

"You have to walk it by yourself"

> "You have to walk that lonesome valley,
> You have to walk it by yourself;
> Oh, nobody else can walk it for you,
> You have to walk it by yourself."

So runs the old spiritual. And so I found it to be.

"It was the loneliness that bothered me," said a friend who had had three operations and then a safety period of five years with no return of the disease. "I think cancer is the loneliest disease in the world. No matter how close family and friends are, they cannot help you, really. In one sense, cancer seems to set you apart in a particularly lonely group where each person is alone."

A minister who had undergone radical surgery wrote me: "It has been worth the suffering to experience personally what so many persons are having to undergo. It is an experience which has to be lived through to be understood. *Now* I can help people because I *know.*"

"God alone can help you," said a friend, dear to me since childhood days, when she visited me to share the experience of radical surgery which came to both of us the same year. "I do not know what people do who do not know how to let God help them."

"You do not have to be concerned about me," I said confidently to a friend who had waited, as I was waiting now, for the report on a set of X-rays six months after the operation. "I settled all this before I left the hospital and I'm ready for whatever is shown." The examination had dragged on for nearly a month; there were symptoms which necessitated the gathering of all X-rays to be examined again. I was sure that I was not tense. Yet when the report came in, tension went out of me like air from an opened balloon! I climbed back on the razor's edge knowing that I still needed daily strengthening for the way I, and several million others, walk alone.

"Religion is what man does with his aloneness."

"There is a sense in which one who has found the beloved community is never alone again."

Both of these statements have come often to mind during this past year. The second one needs its own chapter of consideration.

6.

PRAYER:

"I am not alone . . .
my Father is with me"

"Prayer is simply talking to God. You talk to Him as the One who knows all about you and loves you more than you love yourself. Then you get still inside to hear what He answers."

How thankful I have been through the years to my

parents and to "Miss Allie," an early Sunday school teacher, for teaching me this truth when I was still a child—a truth which has become an increasingly helpful practice through the years. Each person develops his own way of praying. Some which have helped me may not help another person. But I feel led to share a few of the ways prayer has helped one person during months of crisis.

When I first learned of the possibilities of cancer, I stood on a street corner and cried inwardly, "This is too big for me to handle, Father! Please take over!" And I rested in the consciousness that the power at the center of the universe is Love—unselfish, outgoing, redeeming, creative Love. Peace flowed into me and dispelled the panic, peace which I did not "manufacture" and cannot explain.

During the lecture-luncheon, I silently talked out the possibilities that faced me. As I tried to decide what I must do next, I continued to be aware that there were hidden factors which made me need God's wisdom in making any decision. I remember claiming a promise as I silently went over the alternatives: "You have said, 'If any of you lack wisdom, let him ask of God, that giveth to all men liberally, and upbraideth not; and it shall be given him.' I do lack wisdom, and I ask for it very humbly. You have never failed me. I've asked many times before and you have answered whether I recognized the answer at the time or not. I thank you that you will help me know the right thing to do now. The time is short. As soon as I leave this table, I must act. I do not know what I should do. I thank you that I shall know."

By the time the luncheon ended and Margaret and I could talk again, I had several things eliminated and several other common-sense ideas to discuss with her. Moreover, the peace which was better than understanding was extending its sway over my mind, and fear was being so completely conquered that I knew God was taking more and more control.

After finding the surgeon so efficient and capable, I could only give thanks that I had been led aright, and my prayers turned again to requests—for the right person to take my place at the convention, for God's shielding my family from shock—then to thanksgiving that He was able to work in this experience for His glory and the good of all whom the experience might touch.

The night before the operation, I claimed promises, prayed for the old couple, laughed with God about my being "that woman." I was too groggy to think intelligently on the morning of the operation, but I remember that I was comforted and blessed as I fell asleep murmuring a childhood prayer: "Now I lay me down to sleep . . ."

During those days of "riding the waves," I simply claimed promises and gave thanks for present blessings—I was too sick to do more. And I did not need to do more. The peace which had come still held sway. How often I have proved the truth that God takes over when we ask and are not able to do more than ask! God does for us the things we cannot do for ourselves.

There are, however, things which He expects us to do for ourselves, and these He does not do. I found this truth demonstrated again and again during the weeks and months which followed the operation. As strength slowly returned there were things I needed to do about the inner life of prayer.

There was the matter of my own quiet time. A hospital is a place of many interruptions. I soon learned again what I have known for years and years: we can keep our thoughts a conversation with God all day long, only if we keep sacred a definite period of devotion each day. A regular time for private prayer and meditation is necessary—for me at least—if the day is to be spent in awareness of the Presence and if my thoughts are to be kept as a dialogue which gives strength and wisdom, courage and peace.

Then there was reading. As soon as I was strong enough, I started on various types of reading, majoring in things which had some good thoughts but were light enough to keep me relaxed. Friends brought in many kinds of reading matter. I read novels, poetry, and non-fiction. These I interspersed with books of the Old and New Testaments and various types of short devotional readings.

When visitors were limited, because I was tired in mind and body, I changed my reading to "escape material"—and suddenly I became aware that the peace which had been so constant was wearing thin.

During the days of "riding the waves" it was all right not to think. Now that those days were past, the peace which was so freely given was mine to maintain. There must be spiritual thoughts to nourish mind and spirit, or the peace waned. I left the "westerns" and "murder mysteries" and returned to light reading which still had "meat for thought" in it. I had found that escape literature may be used for resting, but a steady diet of it can dull the spirit. The peace of God keeps the heart and mind which are "stayed on Him." In times of weakness as in times of busy-ness or of stress or of commonplace, routine living, there must be a constant return to the Source if the channels are to be kept open enough for the peace of God to flow into life.

There will be times, however, when one is much too sick to read at all, when one must go back to quoting a single verse of Scripture; or, as one improves, to passages one remembers. This clinging to God is still necessary for the maintenance of our peace. God gives; we abide, to keep it alive.

Beyond one's own quiet time, beyond the hours of reading, lies the ministry of intercession. One can either wallow in self-pity and pain, or make constant acts of adoration and thanksgiving and petition for other people. The first way leads to the destruction of peace. The second builds it into a fortress, strong and comforting and sure.

I thought of my friend Mary. After an operation similar to mine, she became the "unpaid chaplain" of the hospital. Patients scheduled conferences; doctors sent her to encourage patients; and she blessed staff and patients and families alike with her cheerful testimony and helpful, Christian counsel. She wrote: "As I walked the corridors, I tried to take the presence of the healing Christ with me; and, as always, He was at work." Her doctors marveled at her quick recovery. Five of them told her that they saw a force at work in her beyond that which was normal. In bringing help to others, she herself grew strong.

A hospital is an easy place in which to pray. There are so many unobtrusive calls to anyone who is aware: the pretty little nurse away from home for the first time and facing popularity without many standards for conduct; the fine young college student working as an orderly to pay expenses; the elderly nurses' aide, so gently kind, so obviously tired; the doctors with their heavy schedules; the nurses and their responsibilities; the inmates of rooms with "No Visitors" signs; the families with drawn, anxious faces—and always, always, the constant, unexpected kindnesses of friends, family, doctors, nurses, and acquaintances, the little nameless acts of love which brighten the days and fill the heart with thanksgiving!

It became increasingly easy for me to follow with prayer all who entered my room, to picture them meeting and overcoming any weakness or seeing them strong in God's strength as they did the work assigned to them.

The celebration of the Lord's Supper has always been a source of strength to me. During the days when I was shut off from corporate worship with the covenant community, I felt the help of the church constantly through continuous remembrances by church groups and individual members, and through the radio services in which I took an active part. But there came a time when I needed more than this. How blessedly I was helped by the young minister to whom I made my needs known! At my request, he came with a young elder, as dear to me as a son, and the three of us shared beside my bed the mystery of the God who acts and who is known still in the broken bread and the poured-out wine. The broken body and the shed blood brought the Eternal very near. I knew again in a new way what Jesus meant when He said, "I am not alone, because the Father is with me." I knew the meaning of the old spiritual:

> "Jesus walks that valley with me,
> I do not walk it by myself;
> Though nobody else can walk it for me,
> I do not walk it by myself."

7.

A SENSE OF HUMOR:

Develop it!

"If you have no sense of humor, begin now to develop one," said a college professor once to a class I attended. "You'll find it furnishes a needed cushion for life in times of stress."

I remembered that the day the little student nurse

paused in her preparation to give me a treatment and said naively, "We'll have to wait for the head nurse to come in. This is the only part of the examination I just can't seem to pass."

"You're tired tonight, aren't you?" Margaret asked one evening.

"I'm tired of comforting people because *I* have cancer," I said.

We laughed together because we knew that I only half meant it, that I was grateful for the love and concern of friends, even though having three weep in one day, who had come "to cheer me up," was a little hard on the nervous system.

People do not know what to say to persons with cancer. Understanding the reasons back of silences or wrong remarks enables one to receive what is meant instead of what is said—but a sense of humor is needed also to keep things in their proportions. One illustration may help someone else to see the humor in a similar situation. This is one of many, chosen at random, because the motivation was love in spite of the comical results.

A well-loved friend who had been sick over the

years was coming to see me. Because I had listened literally by the hour to her symptoms and her reactions to them, her feelings about an incurable illness which had to be borne and the various things the doctors had said to her or tried to do for her, I thought eagerly: "She is one person who knows how this feels. She knows how talking things out helps. I shall be able to get out a few of the things which have been piling up in me during these months since the operation."

When she arrived we talked again of her illness, of her brother-in-law's death, and various other happenings which concerned her children, her husband, or herself. I was genuinely interested. When that was finished, however, I found that I was waiting for her to ask some question about my recent experiences. When none came, I thought, "She is waiting for me to begin," and opened the subject.

"Oh," she said lightly, "you're going to be all right. I know a woman who had that operation twenty years ago and she is all right."

When I ventured to suggest that my case might be a little different, she ignored my remark, saying,

"Did I tell you about . . ." With that, she returned to a former topic.

I confess that at the time I was disappointed, a little hurt, and a little peeved. All that has been changed. I chuckle now each time I think of it. I later learned that she wrote a mutual friend: "I just had to change the subject to keep Myrtle from talking about herself."

And the subject to which she returned? Her brother-in-law's funeral—her brother-in-law who had died of cancer!

A sense of humor cushions life in times of stress!

8.

A NEW ADVENTURE:

Find it!

"Whenever life begins to grow stale, find a new adventure."

The words rang in my mind as the weeks lengthened and the walking between extremes began to wear on the nerves. A new adventure—when the body still gave out at the least exertion? What new adventure could be followed with the physical strength left to me?

I remembered the first one of my friends to demonstrate the new adventure. She gave up a regional position of great importance, retired to an obscure farm with her beloved father, and, with him, took some state university courses in animal husbandry. I remembered her letter: "I felt I could not face this thing in a rootless condition," she wrote. "I have to be with my family, to put down roots in a community, to live a shared life."

Now, the probationary period past, the five years gone by with no return of malignancy, she holds an even greater position of usefulness—so great that she said in confidence, "Without those experiences (some of them during the 'hidden years') I would never have had the courage to tackle this job."

I reread Emily's letter—Emily who visited me during my hospitalization and who found herself, one month after I left the hospital, with an even more painful experience than mine—Emily, whose letter was filled with her plans for working with the

American Cancer Society in an effort to help prevent others from having the experience.

What was to be my new adventure? Suddenly, the door opened by means of a letter from the graduate school where I had planned to spend my "sabbatical year." Because I had registered for the Spring Semester, the Intersession, and the Summer Session, and had been prevented from coming, if I cared to study either New Testament Greek or Old Testament Hebrew, an exception would be made in my case and I could enroll in the Intersession period usually reserved for students in the regular course. A chance to study New Testament Greek! I had wanted it all of my professional life, and here in six weeks' time was a year's course offered—I could learn enough to go on my own. Here was my adventure made to order: If the razor's edge should give way to years of health, this was exactly what I needed in my work; if the path lay straight to the Gate on the far horizon and I had long days to spend in bed, here would be an occupation which would give constant rewarding use of time. For me, the ideal adventure was opening!

I knew then and I know doubly now that each person should find his own new adventure and use it to make life shine again with interest. I arrived in New York spent in body and with a very rusty mind. I found myself in a class with eighteen men—all of them, including the relaxed, capable young professor, young enough to be my sons. Then began six weeks of wonderfully thrilling experience: objective study that demanded every ounce of strength in body and the reawakening of a mind which for several months had been idle. The body made demands that would not be ignored. The hours not spent in class had to be spent in bed—studying or sleeping. The week ends were spent in drugged sleep or in escape reading, with only the eleven o'clock church service to break the resting. As the weeks wore on, even that hour became too much. I was stimulated as I had not been for years with a stimulation that was deep and satisfying. When, at the end of the fifth week, I read the first chapter of First John in Greek, I felt such exaltation as I had not known for years. The fact that I became too tired and could not finish the course for credit did not matter; with the help of lexicons, I can now read the New Testament in its original tongue. I have a relaxing occupation of which I never tire. I have found that my mind can still obey my will, that gray hair does not affect one's ability to learn new things—and that a weakened body does take a toll. But the toll was small in comparison with the great, great gain of my new adventure!

I recommend as heartily as possible to all who are recuperating from an operation for cancer: Find the thing which for you will be a new adventure. Find it and do it and grow happy in the doing of it.

9.

THE RAZOR'S EDGE:

Walk it!

The preceding chapters were written in a three-day burst of energy, following the completion of the period of study described in chapter eight. At that time, the whole plan of the book took definite shape in Myrtle's mind. There were to be twelve chapters in all. Unfortunately, four were never written, and no one can write them now. The best that can be done is for her friends to tell, as simply as possible, how her bout with cancer ended. We believe that this story will carry forward her basic purpose in writing, which was to help others who must face the same dread enemy.

We have retained the title she had chosen for her final chapter. It was often in her mind that the cancer patient must walk a very narrow "razor's edge" between false hope on the one side and despair on the other. He must live with uncertainty as he steps, a day at a time, into an unknown future. This is the story of how she herself walked that lonesome, narrow way, triumphant to the very end of it.

At summer's end Myrtle returned to the College for the fall quarter. She and Margaret arranged to share an apartment. As she tried to move in, she found herself weaker than she had thought, and soon pain had her in its grip again. The symptoms were like those of arthritis. Although she and all her friends suspected the return of malignancy, hospital tests showed nothing positive. After a few days in traction, she returned to the campus and began to teach.

Her consuming interest in her students swept through her like a flood. Her mind was characteristically busy with new ideas, new approaches to the subject, new ways of stimulating "her" freshmen. But the flesh was weak. Climbing the stairs to the classroom left her breathless. Her creative teaching hours were followed by hours of almost complete exhaustion. It was as brave a struggle as ever was fought, and we who loved her stood by, proud of her but powerless to help. She wanted it that way.

The prayed-for strength did not return. Pain increased its grip. After two weeks the gallant soldier was retired from the field and carried once again to the now familiar hospital. Now the razor's edge was sharp indeed. Within the four walls of a hospital room she had to walk it all the rest of the way.

The hardest part came first. For the doctors really did not know. X-rays revealed nothing definite. One by one they exhausted all the other possible explanations of her pain: pleurisy, virus pneumonia . . . And down across the long days and nights she kept on fighting. At first she hoped to return to her classes, and gave those who were substituting for her minute and explicit directions. Then she hoped to return by the opening of the second quarter. Finally it became evident to her and to the doctors that the malignancy was back and that return to the classroom was unlikely.

This realization brought renewed peace. Still she felt it cowardly not to fight. She grew progressively weaker, but her mind remained completely clear. She knew everything and everybody. All visitors were introduced warmly to every nurse, aide, maid, or orderly in sight. Members of the classes she had taught for only two weeks were inquired after by name. Callers exhausted her, yet she wanted to see everyone. She was constantly in prayer, not so much for herself as for them, and her room became a shrine where in her weakness she strengthened others.

Her beloved niece, Mary Clark, arrived for a visit, and was a real benediction. She persuaded Myrtle not to resist the sedatives and narcotics ordered by the doctor. From that time on, pain was not the problem it had been. Myrtle gave Mary Clark explicit directions for her funeral: no grim Scriptures, no sad hymns. Let the theme be: "Rejoice in the Lord, the Lord is at hand." Let the college choir sing the Hallelujah Chorus. Let the congregation sing "Lead On, O King Eternal." No flowers; let the money be given to the College for a small chapel for prayer.

After Mary Clark left there was a great weariness. "How much longer am I supposed to keep trying?" she asked. But the saving sense of humor was still there. It hurt to laugh, but laugh she would. She thoroughly enjoyed startling a friend with the remark: "Suppose after all these preparations, I goof and don't die?"

For her "the new adventure" had become death itself. She spoke of it as her "crowning day," and seemed to have conquered all fear of it.

Now she slept most of the time, but remained perfectly lucid when awake. Her sister-in-law Lois and her nephew Norval were to come two days before Thanksgiving. "It will be too late," she said once. But she waited for them. They came and she talked with them, getting many things settled and off her mind. One of the last things was: "Tell the organist not to drag the hymns." Then she went to sleep. In the early hours of Thanksgiving morning she stepped off the razor's edge forever. She had never lost her balance.

Myrtle Williamson was not a victim of cancer, but a victor over it. True, the disease ravaged her body and did to her its fearful worst. But it never touched the inner citadel of her peace, her courage, her laughter, her faith in God, her abiding interest in other people.

In her will she directed that her eyes be given to the eye-bank. This was done, and today an Alabama sawmill worker sees to work and support his children through her eyes.

Herein is a parable. For she wrote this book in the hope that those who read it will see cancer, and pain, and death through her eyes. To those eyes, all the darkness is shot through with glory.

God Bless You Every One

The following was dictated, slowly and clearly, as Myrtle lay in an oxygen tent a few days before her death, when she knew she would never finish this book...

Humbly I am learning to walk the razor's edge. Starting this book was a big adventure. Nine weeks in the hospital have taught me that I have very, very much to learn. I know that the way is full of pain, that I am still full of pride, and that I am far, far from humble. I submit this book to you with the prayer that God may use it and do with it what He will. I am grateful for His grace, beyond expression. God bless you every one.

"She, being dead, yet speaketh."

Sources of the Scripture quoted in this book

Romans 8:39 (altered slightly)
Romans 8:37 (altered slightly)
Deuteronomy 33:25
Philippians 1:23-24 (Revised Standard Version)
James 1:5
John 16:32
Hebrews 11:4 (adapted)